MW00651875

We were married on date: _____

at location: _____

by: _____

This Book Belongs to:

_____

If found call:

_____

Table of Contents

Hello, I am excited for you and this adventure you are on called MARRIAGE.

I'll bet marriage has been a dream of yours for some time. It is the beginning step to creating a meaningful life with your spouse. It is also the end, or death, of being a single person. When you are married, you unite with the person you choose and create the life you want to live together.

As I write this, I have been married twice for a total of 29 years. I have also worked as a funeral director for 25 years. During this time, I have observed a unique thing. While helping people at the end of their spouse's life, they often share what made their marriage so special. Some of these couples were married for a few years and others for 40, 50, 60, and 70 years. They share with me one or two things they did to create an extraordinary marriage that brought them joy and happiness. These important ideas made their marriage work and thrive.

When I heard the decisions they made about their marriage, I took the ideas home and shared then with my wife. We would discuss these habits and either make them our own or tweak them to fit our marriage. Now, not all of the spouses I met had marriages that created joy and happiness. Some were filled with headaches and problems too.

These conversations gave me valuable information to share with my wife, so we also learned what not to do. Once we understood the detrimental results of not working together as a team, we made changes to reduce the chance of creating trouble in our marriage.

After hearing stories of happy and sad marriages, I asked myself, what is the purpose of marriage? Why were these successfully married people different?

They were there to help each other grow in understanding, sacrifice, communication, and confidence. To believe in each other, strengthen faith, give and receive compassion, enjoy joy, happiness, and create peace. When love is added to the mix it helped them learn to grow together.

I believe that in this book you'll find the tools you need to create a marriage that lasts the ages.

Let's get started building the dream. ~Steven Wells

When two people come together and make a decision to get married, two people who are genuinely committed to helping each other become the best person they can be, they each grow to their fullest potential. If they don't work together, they can become the worst person, and also help their spouse become the worst they can be. Everything has a life cycle, and if your life is growing and flourishing, then it is productive. If it is not growing and thriving, then it is in a state of deterioration and, eventually, death.

When married, we gain a confidant, coach, and companion to whom we feel a deep connection. Our union creates an opportunity to continue to learn as a person and to grow in awareness and knowledge.

Climbing a Mountain Together

Your marriage is like climbing a mountain. It's easy to imagine what the view from the top will be, but the problem is getting there. It helps to have an end in mind when you are climbing and to do what is necessary to reach the top. The path is right in front of you, and the sign says to "go this way," but it appears to be a hard climb. Are you willing to take the next step and start walking?

The real end is hidden from view, and you will not know what lies in the path ahead, and what will cross your path as you make the journey to the top. While you are walking, you will meet other people who are coming down the trail. They might tell you that the view is worth it, to keep going even though it might get tough, or they might say the trek is just too hard; that no view is worth the amount of effort.

Who will you listen to? Will you let someone else influence your decision to get to the top of the mountain? Will their suggestions be enough for you to say, Okay I've had it, I am turning back.

Marriage is a unique path. The beautiful thing is that it is yours. It is what you make out of it. I want to share with you what I have learned and help you understand some of the elements that go into creating a marriage that thrives with joy and happiness.

My goal is to give you the strength to endure whatever tests life may throw your way. I'll help you understand you are creating this life together and that the decisions and choices you make will have a consequence. The consequence I want for you is the dream life you want.

As you both work together in this journal, you will create the path that is needed to arrive at your view of marriage after 25 years. It will be your guide, so you are sure to choose and remain on the track that leads to success. This journal will help you see when you strayed off the path so that you can do a course correction. As you look back, you'll see how far you have come from the day you said: "I do."

The marriage journal gives you a chance to change the direction you're heading when you become aware of something new you both want. That's okay. Your marriage is a journey. Working together will help you become aware of new things and opportunities you couldn't see from where you are standing at the beginning.

The Goal is a Long and Happy Marriage

What will your view look like after 25 years of marriage? What is the expectation of your life together 25 years from now? Don't be like a lot of the spouses I have met who didn't know where they wanted to go. Not taking the time to plan leads to defeat, with diverging paths (growing apart), or turning around and giving up (divorce).

The unhappy people that I talked to didn't create life; they received what life gave them. We all have tools to live the way we want happiness to be; we need to be more aware of these tools and learn how to use them. I've found that most of us are not using these tools as efficiently as we could. It takes effort and a willingness to use them, to make them work in your life. My wife and I are still learning how to use ours effectively, more than likely, so are you.

Marriage is About Giving and Receiving

Think about that; life is about giving and receiving—what better place to learn this than in marriage. Marriage is about giving and receiving love, compassion, kindness, and support. As your life goes from one day to the next, you will give of yourself to help your spouse. You'll also receive help from your spouse. Be grateful for the support you receive from each other and other people.

You would not be together without the help of other people. You both have parents, and they made you. Every teacher, coach, or mentor has given of their time and talents to teach you the things they have learned and experienced in life so far. You received and instilled those values, morals, and experiences, and they are inside of you right now. It has all come from someone else being willing to give something they had to you. You helped them by receiving what they were teaching and the help they offered you.

Being a couple allows you to learn from each other. Giving and receiving is not about keeping score. Instead, it is about growing as a person, and as a strong couple that can withstand all this world will throw at you. Giving allows you to be grateful for each other, to have unconditional love, to learn forgiveness, to honor each other, to be less selfish of your wants. You'll learn how to work with your chosen partner to create the life you want to live.

Write it Down

Take the time to write down your dreams; this viewpoint is vital. When you write it down, it becomes a decision. Journaling helps you become more committed to the position you want, more than just expressing it out loud does. This journal is the starting location for your dreams.

While hiking the mountain, you need a map for your trip to the top. You have a starting point and an endpoint. During your travel from point A to point B, there can be many different roads, exits, on-ramps, and right and left turns to make. If you didn't know where you were going, you will just flow with whatever happens and end up wherever you stopped. Your life together is no different. You are at the starting point, and this journal will help you create the endpoint.

When you describe where your life is going, the steps to take will become apparent. When you express your future life in this book, use as much detail as you can. Add to the dream over the years. Clarify the details as you gain more information about what you want to acquire. Writing it down is the first step.

Where Will You Be in 25 Years?

In the following pages you'll write down your view of your marriage after 25 years. Don't worry about figuring out how it will happen. The help you need will be there when you need it. If you look back over your life now, you'll see that you have been helped all along the way. It may or may not have been what you wanted or expected, but help was there. Have faith and expect this dream to come into your life as you create it.

When you read the ideas you've written in this journal 25 years from now, you will realize this is true. It has happened in my life, and I don't believe I am any different than you.

Danger Ahead

Before you start any journey, you want to know what dangers may lie ahead. Marriage is no different. Knowing what to do and not to do prepares you for the trip. Here are some of the things I learned from the spouses that I interviewed. Each situation is something that gives advice or instruction on what to look out for in your first 25 years of marriage. These obstacles will help you prepare, just as my wife and I did.

When you get married, you make vows to one another. These vows have meaning and life to them; they are not just words shared between two people. Marriage vows are the beginning of creating life the way you want it to be.

What to Pack in your Bags, What to Leave Behind

You'll also need to pack your bags when you start on this journey. You have items to bring to your new life and home. Perhaps you have favorite things from your past that you carry around with you with each move. Ask yourself why they are important.

I have an old football jersey that has been in my closet for years. It's next to my FFA jacket. Why hold on to it for so long? It helps me remind me of the things I learned in my youth. They remind me of the triumphs of my childhood.

Many of the things from your youth will not help in the future. They are, however, lessons that can teach you what not to do. Learn from those lessons and make an effort to change, because these things you are holding on to from the past don't serve you.

One thing to pack in your bags is the ability to compromise. You are each unique individuals with different desires that need fulfillment. When you are happy individually, happiness will overflow into your marriage.

Pack your bags carefully; marriage is not just about you. You are moving from "me" to "us," and how you think and act has to be from the US point of view. When you see clearly, nothing can stop you from working together to create and build your dreams.

What do you need to leave behind as you are entering this new phase of your life?

_____

_____

_____

_____

_____

_____

_____

_____

_____

_____

_____

Dump the Garbage

After you pack your bags, dump the garbage. These are the habits and ideas that can hold you back from getting to where you want to be in 25 years. They do not help you. During your first years of marriage, you will need to do some repeated cleaning and dumping as the old garbage creeps back into your life. Getting rid of the trash that is holding you back, helps to clear space for the things that will move your marriage to where you want to be.

Here's an example: I used to drink socially, but the last time I drank, I caused a bunch of trouble. Not just for me but the other people around me. After I thought about it for a couple of weeks, I made the decision never to drink again. Not drinking has been one of the greatest things I did for my life.

Don't pack your bad habits and bring them along into your marriage, especially if you know they haven't helped you move towards your dreams. Understand that if something isn't helping you get to where you want to go, you need to change what you are doing. You decided to be married to your spouse. Some of your old ways need to become just that - old ways.

If you are unsure of what should be considered garbage, ask yourself these questions.

- ❏   Will this idea or habit help me get to where I want to go?
- ❏   Is this habit or item strengthening my marriage relationship or hindering it?

It may be hard for you to dump some habits, but doing so allows you to create new patterns and acquire new things. These new habits will move you forward and help you create your dream.

Creating Rules

> "It's your game: make up your own rules." Barbara Corcoran

What do I mean when I say there are rules in a marriage? Well, you already have unspoken rules in your relationship, but you likely have unconsciously made them. When you know you have rules for your relationship, and you make them together, they are easy to follow and become who you are as a couple.

Examples of rules you might want to adopt:
- ❏   Always hold hands when you walk together, watch a movie, or drive in a car together.
- ❏   Offer a kiss when you see each other or when you leave. (Eventually, your children will call you out when you miss doing this.)
- ❏   Give a courtesy phone call when you are heading home from an activity, traveling or when you leave work.
- ❏   Set a specific night as date night, and do something fun together.

- ❑ Say prayers together before going to bed
- ❑ Exchange chores - one takes out the garbage every week, and the other will make the bed every day.
- ❑ One sleeps on the right side of the bed, and the other on the left. (If you don't think this one is a rule, then try sleeping on the alternate side of the bed for one night. Either you will switch sides mid-way, or it will be a bad night of sleep. I tried that once, and that was a mistake.)
- ❑ Make a deal for watching all of the football or sports you want, after chores get done for the day.

What rules do you have? What ones are you going to create?

Taking the time to make rules as a couple will strengthen your decision-making ability. Making choices that support your decisions will bring into view what you expect to have. Rules will keep you moving in the same direction as each other.

They do not hinder or degrade the other person. You both agree to these rules because there is an expectation you want to achieve from them. The rules you create will be the design to strengthen your relationship.

The coolest thing is now you are aware of them, you can discuss what rules you want to have. You can change them up as your life changes. Change is always happening in your life, and change is good. Make sure they bring growth to your relationship and don't hold you back.

Write down some couple rules you already do and those you want to adopt

_____

_____

_____

_____

_____

_____

_____

_____

Creating the Life You Both Want

This journal gives you a place to imagine your life together, but thinking with the end in mind trips up most people. You might find it hard to decide how you want your life to unfold. Many people believe they can't get what they want and instead think there are limitations to what can be achieved. Don't you believe it! Yes, you will make some mistakes in getting to your dream life. Those mistakes and failures are lessons that will teach you and make your marriage stronger. Take what you learn from talking together and apply it to your plans, you'll be less likely to make the mistakes again.

A strong marriage is based on responding to problems rather than reacting to them. You want to be able to handle what life throws at you. If you don't know where you are going, then how do you know the best response? A climber climbing a mountain knows where they are starting from and where they are trying to reach. Whether the journey is a success depends on their willingness to use the tools they brought with them. Decide how your life will look. What will be in it? How you will contribute to this world and what experiences you will enjoy as a couple?

Writing it down in this journal and reviewing it yearly will help you verify you are on the right path, and will help you get the life of your dreams. We all have different aspirations for our marriage, working careers, and hobbies. One is not better or worse than the other, they are just different. You get to choose what experiences, hobbies, jobs, and relationships you want in your life. Don't let fear, doubt, and discouragement get in the way.

How to Use the Journal Pages

In the next few pages you'll find worksheets to guide you through several areas of your life. Answer the upcoming questions with as much detail as you can.

Start by creating the view for your marriage 25 years in the future. Imagine what you will see as you look back at your life from the pinnacle of the mountain you are climbing. You will, at that time, see all of the accomplishments you have made.

Then come back to these yearly pages on your anniversary and add to them. You'll write down the highlights of the last year and assess how you are doing as you head towards the ultimate goal. As you review and ascend to your 25-year viewpoint, other ideas and plans will come into view. Be sure to add those so they can grow your relationship.

Time - Till Death Do Us Part

Death is going to happen! One of you will die before the other one. You may not want to think or talk about death; most couples don't, but not talking about it will not stop that day from coming. You will eventually have to say goodbye to each other.

Time is significant; you don't know how much you will have. We don't think about how much time there is because there will always be tomorrow, right. If you are not planning the activities that you are doing in the amount of time given to you, you may run out of time together. There will be regrets, even regrets for not doing meaningful things to help your spouse. Are there activities you are willing to do to make the most out of the time you will spend together? The time you have is for sharing life. It will include your daily activities, significant accomplishments, disappointments, happiness, struggles, joy, discouragement, fear, and growth. What are you going to do with your time together?

There was a young man who got married, and he and his wife talked and dreamed of the life they would have together. They believed they had many years to fulfill their dreams. Three months into their marriage, they got the news that she had cancer. Suddenly the priorities of their marriage changed and being together was of the utmost importance.

That man was me. The next three years were tough but very rewarding. We worked together, made decisions together, and did the best we could under the circumstances. We lived life to the fullest and made the best out of the time we had left. I look back on this time of my life without regrets.

Live Each Day As If It Were a Gift

One day as I was finishing a funeral arrangement with Paul he shared how deeply he had loved his wife, Clair, ever since the day he met her. They had a great life, very rarely argued, talked a lot, and never went to bed angry at each other. You see, he met his wife when she was dating another guy and when he found out that she was engaged, he was heartbroken. He had fallen in love with her and never had the chance to date her!

Several months later, he found out that he was in luck; she was single again. He asked Clair to go out on a date, and it didn't take him long to ask her to become his wife. Before she said yes, she had one condition - could Paul live with knowing that she might die in an instant? She didn't know when only that she would die in an instant. Paul told her that if she became his wife, he would make each day they had together special.

Paul's wife, Clair, was killed in an instant on a sunny morning as she walked to her mailbox. He had decided right at the beginning of their marriage that each day would be a gift and he did this for over 50 years. Every morning he asked himself what he would do if this was their last day together and then set about making it a day without arguments and regrets, only love. Paul said that every time a little thing would start to bother him, he would ask if it was necessary to get angry over it.

The act of treating each day as if it was their last, helped them build a solid relationship, and the last day they had together was as good as the first.

Your time together is for creating the life of your dreams. It doesn't have to conform to what anyone else says or thinks it should look. It's your life together; you share it and are creating every moment.

What you create is done each day you work together. You can move your dream life into reality. It starts when you both follow the decisions you make together. Choosing the activities that support your choices in the time you are given will make your dream a reality.

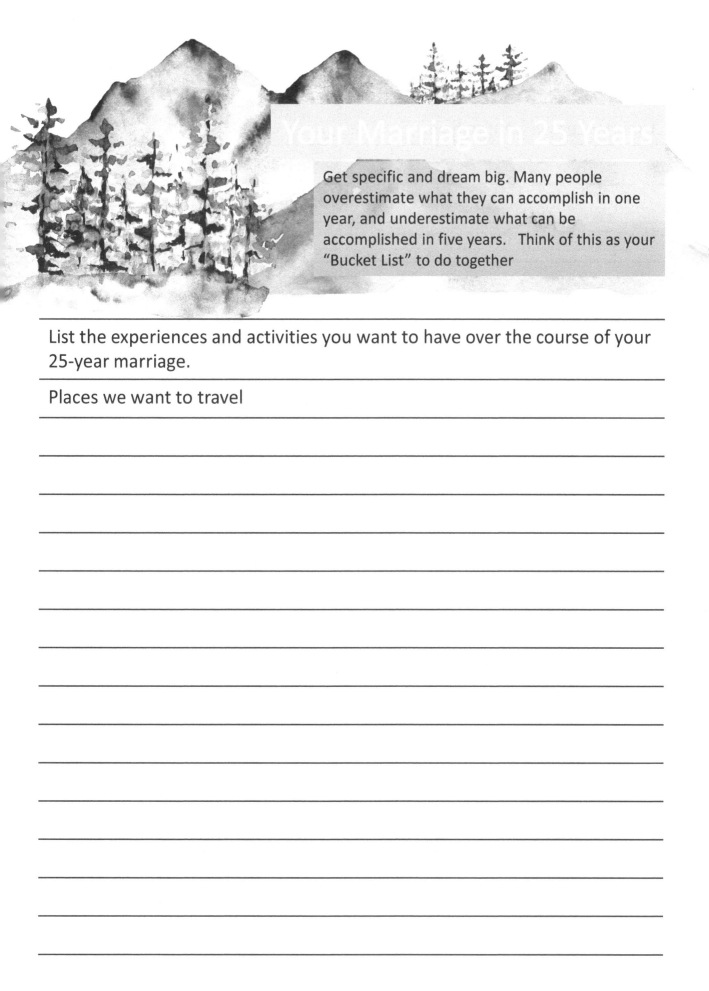

Your Marriage in 25 Years

Get specific and dream big. Many people overestimate what they can accomplish in one year, and underestimate what can be accomplished in five years. Think of this as your "Bucket List" to do together

List the experiences and activities you want to have over the course of your 25-year marriage.

Places we want to travel

More experiences and activities

Experiences we want to have:

Year 10 REVIEW

Date: _____

Relationships, Rules, Giving: To Love and To Cherish
What relationship milestones did you accomplish in the past year? How are you giving of yourself to others?

_____

_____

_____

_____

_____

_____

_____

Are there any new rules you need to create to help your marriage be stronger?

_____

_____

_____

_____

_____

_____

_____

_____

Year 11 REVIEW

Date: _____

Relationships, Rules, Giving: To Love and To Cherish

What relationship milestones did you accomplish in the past year? How are you giving of yourself to others?

_____

_____

_____

_____

_____

_____

_____

_____

Are there any new rules you need to create to help your marriage be stronger?

_____

_____

_____

_____

_____

_____

_____

_____

_____

Year 12 REVIEW

Date: _____

Relationships, Rules, Giving: To Love and To Cherish
What relationship milestones did you accomplish in the past year? How are you giving of yourself to others?

_____

_____

_____

_____

_____

_____

_____

_____

Are there any new rules you need to create to help your marriage be stronger?

_____

_____

_____

_____

_____

_____

_____

_____

_____

Year 13 REVIEW

Date: _____

Relationships, Rules, Giving: To Love and To Cherish
What relationship milestones did you accomplish in the past year? How are you giving of yourself to others?

_____

_____

_____

_____

_____

_____

_____

Are there any new rules you need to create to help your marriage be stronger?

_____

_____

_____

_____

_____

_____

_____

_____

_____

Year 14 REVIEW

Date: _____

Relationships, Rules, Giving: To Love and To Cherish
What relationship milestones did you accomplish in the past year? How are you giving of yourself to others?

_____

_____

_____

_____

_____

_____

_____

_____

Are there any new rules you need to create to help your marriage be stronger?

_____

_____

_____

_____

_____

_____

_____

_____

_____

Year 15 REVIEW

Date: _____

Relationships, Rules, Giving: To Love and To Cherish
What relationship milestones did you accomplish in the past year? How are you giving of yourself to others?

_____

_____

_____

_____

_____

_____

_____

_____

Are there any new rules you need to create to help your marriage be stronger?

_____

_____

_____

_____

_____

_____

_____

_____

_____

Year 16 REVIEW

Date: _____

Relationships, Rules, Giving: To Love and To Cherish
What relationship milestones did you accomplish in the past year? How are you giving of yourself to others?

_____

_____

_____

_____

_____

_____

_____

Are there any new rules you need to create to help your marriage be stronger?

_____

_____

_____

_____

_____

_____

_____

_____

Year 17 REVIEW

Date: _____

Relationships, Rules, Giving: To Love and To Cherish
What relationship milestones did you accomplish in the past year? How are you giving of yourself to others?

_____

_____

_____

_____

_____

_____

_____

Are there any new rules you need to create to help your marriage be stronger?

_____

_____

_____

_____

_____

_____

_____

Year 18 REVIEW

Date: _____

Relationships, Rules, Giving: To Love and To Cherish
What relationship milestones did you accomplish in the past year? How are you giving of yourself to others?

_____

_____

_____

_____

_____

_____

_____

Are there any new rules you need to create to help your marriage be stronger?

_____

_____

_____

_____

_____

_____

_____

_____

Year 19 REVIEW

Date: _____

Relationships, Rules, Giving: To Love and To Cherish
What relationship milestones did you accomplish in the past year? How are you giving of yourself to others?

_____

_____

_____

_____

_____

_____

_____

_____

Are there any new rules you need to create to help your marriage be stronger?

_____

_____

_____

_____

_____

_____

_____

_____

_____

Year 20 REVIEW

Date: _____

Relationships, Rules, Giving: To Love and To Cherish

What relationship milestones did you accomplish in the past year? How are you giving of yourself to others?

_____

_____

_____

_____

_____

_____

_____

_____

Are there any new rules you need to create to help your marriage be stronger?

_____

_____

_____

_____

_____

_____

_____

_____

_____

Year 21 REVIEW

Date: _____

Relationships, Rules, Giving: To Love and To Cherish
What relationship milestones did you accomplish in the past year? How are you giving of yourself to others?

_____

_____

_____

_____

_____

_____

_____

Are there any new rules you need to create to help your marriage be stronger?

_____

_____

_____

_____

_____

_____

_____

_____

Year 22 REVIEW

Date: _____

Relationships, Rules, Giving: To Love and To Cherish
What relationship milestones did you accomplish in the past year? How are you giving of yourself to others?

_____

_____

_____

_____

_____

_____

_____

_____

Are there any new rules you need to create to help your marriage be stronger?

_____

_____

_____

_____

_____

_____

_____

_____

_____

Year 23 REVIEW

Date: _____

Relationships, Rules, Giving: To Love and To Cherish
What relationship milestones did you accomplish in the past year? How are you giving of yourself to others?

_____

_____

_____

_____

_____

_____

_____

_____

Are there any new rules you need to create to help your marriage be stronger?

_____

_____

_____

_____

_____

_____

_____

_____

_____

Year 24 REVIEW

Date: _____

Relationships, Rules, Giving: To Love and To Cherish
What relationship milestones did you accomplish in the past year? How are you giving of yourself to others?

_____

_____

_____

_____

_____

_____

_____

_____

Are there any new rules you need to create to help your marriage be stronger?

_____

_____

_____

_____

_____

_____

_____

_____

Year 25 REVIEW

Date: _____

Relationships, Rules, Giving: To Love and To Cherish
What relationship milestones did you accomplish in the past year? How are you giving of yourself to others?

_____

_____

_____

_____

_____

_____

_____

_____

Are there any new rules you need to create to help your marriage be stronger?

_____

_____

_____

_____

_____

_____

_____

_____

Our Master Bucket List

List the hobbies, trips, activities and other experiences you want to do together over the next 25 years. Use this as your master "Bucket List" to see the things you've planned at a glance.

Add Date	Description	Completed

Our Master Bucket List

List the hobbies, trips, activities and other experiences you want to do together over the next 25 years. Use this as your master "Bucket List" to see the things you've planned at a glance.

Add Date	Description	Completed

Our Master Bucket List

List the hobbies, trips, activities and other experiences you want to do together over the next 25 years. Use this as your master "Bucket List" to see the things you've planned at a glance.

Add Date	Description	Completed

Our Master Bucket List

List the hobbies, trips, activities and other experiences you want to do together over the next 25 years. Use this as your master "Bucket List" to see the things you've planned at a glance.

Add Date	Description	Completed

Our Master Bucket List

List the hobbies, trips, activities and other experiences you want to do together over the next 25 years. Use this as your master "Bucket List" to see the things you've planned at a glance.

Add Date	Description	Completed

Our Master Bucket List

List the hobbies, trips, activities and other experiences you want to do together over the next 25 years. Use this as your master "Bucket List" to see the things you've planned at a glance.

Add Date	Description	Completed

More experiences and activities

Ways we want to treat each other:

_____

_____

_____

_____

_____

_____

_____

_____

_____

_____

_____

_____

_____

_____

_____

_____

_____

More experiences and activities

Add to this list each year as you do your review

_____

_____

_____

_____

_____

_____

_____

_____

_____

_____

_____

_____

_____

_____

_____

_____

_____

_____

_____

More experiences and activities

Add to this list each year as you do your review

_____

_____

_____

_____

_____

_____

_____

_____

_____

_____

_____

_____

_____

_____

_____

_____

_____

_____

Your Home

Describe your **home and where you want to live**. Be sure to talk about the type of house you want and the elements you want in and around it. Do you want a hot tub or pool? How about a craft room, media room, gardens, or a man cave? Do you want to live in the city or out in the country? Do you want a vacation home? Will you have a starter home as you work your way up to the dream or rent an apartment as you save?

More Home Planning

Our Homes

Home address:

Time lived there:

What we liked about this place, Our least favorite thing.

Home address:

Time lived there:

What we liked about this place, Our least favorite thing.

Home address:

Time lived there:

What we liked about this place, Our least favorite thing.

Home address:

Time lived there:

What we liked about this place, Our least favorite thing.

Our Homes

Home address:

Time lived there:

What we liked about this place, Our least favorite thing.

Home address:

Time lived there:

What we liked about this place, Our least favorite thing.

Home address:

Time lived there:

What we liked about this place, Our least favorite thing.

Home address:

Time lived there:

What we liked about this place, Our least favorite thing.

Our Homes

Home address:

Time lived there:

What we liked about this place, Our least favorite thing.

Home address:

Time lived there:

What we liked about this place, Our least favorite thing.

Home address:

Time lived there:

What we liked about this place, Our least favorite thing.

Home address:

Time lived there:

What we liked about this place, Our least favorite thing.

Year 1 REVIEW

Date: _____

Time: Till Death Do Us Part
Review the list of experiences you wanted to have in your marriage. Have you accomplished any of them over the past year? Add these items to the master list.

Add Date	Description	Completed

Are there items you want to add to your list? Use the space below to add new things to experience and accomplish.

Add Date	Description	Completed

Year 2 REVIEW

Date: _____

Time: Till Death Do Us Part
Review the list of experiences you wanted to have in your marriage. Have you accomplished any of them over the past year? Add any new items to the master list.

Add Date	Description	Completed

Are there items you want to add to your list? Use the space below to add new things to experience and accomplish.

Add Date	Description	Completed

Year 3 REVIEW

Date: _____

Time: Till Death Do Us Part
Review the list of experiences you wanted to have in your marriage. Have you accomplished any of them over the past year? Add any new items to the master list.

Add Date	Description	Completed

Are there items you want to add to your list? Use the space below to add new things to experience and accomplish.

Add Date	Description	Completed

Year 4 REVIEW

Date: _____

Time: Till Death Do Us Part
Review the list of experiences you wanted to have in your marriage. Have you accomplished any of them over the past year? Add any new items to the master list.

Add Date	Description	Completed

Are there items you want to add to your list? Use the space below to add new things to experience and accomplish.

Add Date	Description	Completed

Year 5 REVIEW

Date: _____

Time: Till Death Do Us Part

Review the list of experiences you wanted to have in your marriage. Have you accomplished any of them over the past year? Add any new items to the master list.

Add Date	Description	Completed

Are there items you want to add to your list? Use the space below to add new things to experience and accomplish.

Add Date	Description	Completed

Year 6 REVIEW

Date: _____

Time: Till Death Do Us Part
Review the list of experiences you wanted to have in your marriage. Have you accomplished any of them over the past year? Add any new items to the master list.

Add Date	Description	Completed

Are there items you want to add to your list? Use the space below to add new things to experience and accomplish.

Add Date	Description	Completed

Year 7 REVIEW

Date: _____

Time: Till Death Do Us Part
Review the list of experiences you wanted to have in your marriage. Have you accomplished any of them over the past year? Add any new items to the master list.

Add Date	Description	Completed

Are there items you want to add to your list? Use the space below to add new things to experience and accomplish.

Add Date	Description	Completed

Year 8 REVIEW

Date: _____

Time: Till Death Do Us Part
Review the list of experiences you wanted to have in your marriage. Have you accomplished any of them over the past year? Add any new items to the master list.

Add Date	Description	Completed

Are there items you want to add to your list? Use the space below to add new things to experience and accomplish.

Add Date	Description	Completed

Year 9 REVIEW

Date: _____

Time: Till Death Do Us Part
Review the list of experiences you wanted to have in your marriage. Have you accomplished any of them over the past year? Add any new items to the master list.

Add Date	Description	Completed

Are there items you want to add to your list? Use the space below to add new things to experience and accomplish.

Add Date	Description	Completed

Year 10 REVIEW

Date: _____

Time: Till Death Do Us Part
Review the list of experiences you wanted to have in your marriage. Have you accomplished any of them over the past year? Add any new items to the master list.

Add Date	Description	Completed

Are there items you want to add to your list? Use the space below to add new things to experience and accomplish.

Add Date	Description	Completed

Year 11 REVIEW

Date: _____

Time: Till Death Do Us Part
Review the list of experiences you wanted to have in your marriage. Have you accomplished any of them over the past year? Add any new items to the master list.

Add Date	Description	Completed

Are there items you want to add to your list? Use the space below to add new things to experience and accomplish.

Add Date	Description	Completed

Year 12 REVIEW

Date: _____

Time: Till Death Do Us Part

Review the list of experiences you wanted to have in your marriage. Have you accomplished any of them over the past year? Add any new items to the master list.

Add Date	Description	Completed

Are there items you want to add to your list?

Use the space below to add new things to experience and accomplish.

Add Date	Description	Completed

Year 13 REVIEW

Date: _____

Time: Till Death Do Us Part

Review the list of experiences you wanted to have in your marriage. Have you accomplished any of them over the past year? Add any new items to the master list.

Add Date	Description	Completed

Are there items you want to add to your list? Use the space below to add new things to experience and accomplish.

Add Date	Description	Completed

Year 14 REVIEW

Date: _____

Time: Till Death Do Us Part
Review the list of experiences you wanted to have in your marriage. Have you accomplished any of them over the past year? Add any new items to the master list.

Add Date	Description	Completed

Are there items you want to add to your list? Use the space below to add new things to experience and accomplish.

Add Date	Description	Completed

Year 15 REVIEW

Date: _____

Time: Till Death Do Us Part
Review the list of experiences you wanted to have in your marriage. Have you accomplished any of them over the past year? Add any new items to the master list.

Add Date	Description	Completed

Are there items you want to add to your list? Use the space below to add new things to experience and accomplish.

Add Date	Description	Completed

Year 16 REVIEW

Date: _____

Time: Till Death Do Us Part

Review the list of experiences you wanted to have in your marriage. Have you accomplished any of them over the past year? Add any new items to the master list.

Add Date	Description	Completed

Are there items you want to add to your list? Use the space below to add new things to experience and accomplish.

Add Date	Description	Completed

Year 17 REVIEW

Date: _____

Time: Till Death Do Us Part
Review the list of experiences you wanted to have in your marriage. Have you accomplished any of them over the past year? Add any new items to the master list.

Add Date	Description	Completed

Are there items you want to add to your list? Use the space below to add new things to experience and accomplish.

Add Date	Description	Completed

Year 18 REVIEW

Date: _____

Time: Till Death Do Us Part
Review the list of experiences you wanted to have in your marriage. Have you accomplished any of them over the past year? Add any new items to the master list.

Add Date	Description	Completed

Are there items you want to add to your list? Use the space below to add new things to experience and accomplish.

Add Date	Description	Completed

Year 19 REVIEW

Date: _____

Time: Till Death Do Us Part
Review the list of experiences you wanted to have in your marriage. Have you accomplished any of them over the past year? Add any new items to the master list.

Add Date	Description	Completed

Are there items you want to add to your list? Use the space below to add new things to experience and accomplish.

Add Date	Description	Completed

Year 20 REVIEW

Date: _____

Time: Till Death Do Us Part
Review the list of experiences you wanted to have in your marriage. Have you accomplished any of them over the past year? Add any new items to the master list.

Add Date	Description	Completed

Are there items you want to add to your list? Use the space below to add new things to experience and accomplish.

Add Date	Description	Completed

Year 21 REVIEW

Date: _____

Time: Till Death Do Us Part

Review the list of experiences you wanted to have in your marriage. Have you accomplished any of them over the past year? Add any new items to the master list.

Add Date	Description	Completed

Are there items you want to add to your list? Use the space below to add new things to experience and accomplish.

Add Date	Description	Completed

Date: _____

Time: Till Death Do Us Part
Review the list of experiences you wanted to have in your marriage. Have you accomplished any of them over the past year? Add any new items to the master list.

Add Date	Description	Completed

Are there items you want to add to your list? Use the space below to add new things to experience and accomplish.

Add Date	Description	Completed

Year 23 REVIEW

Date: _____

Time: Till Death Do Us Part
Review the list of experiences you wanted to have in your marriage. Have you accomplished any of them over the past year? Add any new items to the master list.

Add Date	Description	Completed

Are there items you want to add to your list? Use the space below to add new things to experience and accomplish.

Add Date	Description	Completed

Year 24 REVIEW

Date: _____

Time: Till Death Do Us Part
Review the list of experiences you wanted to have in your marriage. Have you accomplished any of them over the past year? Add any new items to the master list.

Add Date	Description	Completed

Are there items you want to add to your list? Use the space below to add new things to experience and accomplish.

Add Date	Description	Completed

Year 25 REVIEW

Date: _____

Time: Till Death Do Us Part
Review the list of experiences you wanted to have in your marriage. Have you accomplished any of them over the past year? Add any new items to the master list.

Add Date	Description	Completed

Are there items you want to add to your list? Use the space below to add new things to experience and accomplish.

Add Date	Description	Completed

In Sickness and Health

You know that one of you might die before the other. Sickness could be the cause of it. You may have asked the illness to become part of your life by the choices you made about your health. It may be a sickness, it could be from an accident, or for no explainable reason.

What matters is how you respond. It doesn't matter whether you caused it or if it is unexpected, it will affect your marriage. Illness is a struggle and a test of your relationship. Make sure you are continually building a healthy, supportive, foundational relationship every day.

Don't think negative thoughts about your spouse. You chose this person to walk beside you and counsel with you. Negative thoughts lead you in the wrong direction. Take help from your spouse to gain the strength you need to overcome and adjust your lives to whatever sickness may come.

I met Fred who wanted to get his affairs in order because he had lung cancer; he never smoked a day in his life and had never lived with anyone that smoked. When he found out he had cancer, he and his wife decided to change their life. They lived each day as if it was the last for him. After three years, his doctors were amazed at the progression. His cancer had stopped growing and having it may have slowed him down but did not stop him.

The last time I saw him, he told me he was fulfilling a dream to live next door to his grandkids. He was moving out of state and looking forward to creating cherished memories with them. When you both are healthy, your whole life and relationships are better.

I met with Victoria to make funeral arrangements for her husband. She told me of her desire to go on a cruise from the time they were married. Her husband, Donald, never wanted to and wouldn't let her go with friends. Their marriage was full of resentment about not doing the things they originally dreamed they would do. Donald's health had been poor for much of their marriage because he wouldn't take care of himself. He was overweight and wouldn't move or exercise. He finally said he would go on a cruise for their 25th wedding anniversary, but he died suddenly a few days before the trip.

Victoria decided to hold his funeral on their anniversary date since friends and family were gathering for their party and renewing of vows. She wasn't able to go on her cruise with her husband, and they ran out of time. I often think about how their relationship would have been if they went on their voyage on their first anniversary instead of waiting. Would their relationship have grown in affection each year instead of resentment?

Health is a Choice

Health is a choice that works better when you both are on the same page. Do you need to stop eating foods or get rid of habits that are harmful to your health? You influence each other, and it is hard when one of you chooses not to be supportive when the other is trying to change their health. When you work together, you bring out the best person you can be.

Your health image may be based on your experiences from when you were young. Why not decide on better health right now? Set a goal and decide how long will you live. If you decide that you are going to live to be 100, how will that look? I have been going to nursing homes for years, and as I leave, I always tell myself, that's not me. I do not want to live life in a nursing home, waiting to die. My wife and I decided that we will live to be 100. We will be active, healthy, and strong, able to live in our own home, travel, enjoy our grandkids, and continue to learn. We believe this is possible.

We waited 25 years to make this decision, and have started to make changes. It isn't a fast change, in fact it's much slower than what we want. We didn't get to where we are overnight and the changes we make will take time. We can do it together.

It takes a decision and choices to make your health the way you want it, so dream about how it will look when you are 100. Society tells us as we get old, we shrivel up and die. Why do you want this in your life? Dream about your health and life as you wish, not how society tells you it should be. You should have a different vision than society has. *Nothing is stopping you.*

Health and Fitness: 25 years may seem far away, but it will come in the blink of an eye. On the next page, set your intentions for living a full life and imagine yourself in 25 years. How do you move, eat, exercise, and enjoy life in this older body?

Bride	Groom
Today I am ___ years old	Today I am ___ years old
In 25 years I will be ___ years old	In 25 years I will be ___ years old
This is how I will look and act when I am 25 years older:	This is how I will look and act when I am 25 years older:
These are the changes I need to make to get there:	These are the changes I need to make to get there:
These are the things that I should keep doing:	These are the things that I should keep doing:
This is the help I need:	This is the help I need:

Year 1 REVIEW

Date: _____

In Sickness and in Health

Take a picture of yourselves as a couple. Having a yearly view will allow you to see the changes that are happening over time and make course corrections. Make note of your health success and challenges over the past year.

Today _____ is _____ years old and _____ is _____ years old

_____

_____

_____

_____

_____

_____

_____

What changes do you need to make? Course correction is easier before it gets out of control!

_____

_____

_____

_____

_____

_____

_____

_____

_____

Year 2 REVIEW

Date: _____

In Sickness and in Health

Take a picture of yourselves as a couple. Having a yearly view will allow you to see the changes that are happening over time and make course corrections. Make note of your health success and challenges over the past year.

Today _____ is _____ years old and _____ is _____ years old

_____

_____

_____

_____

_____

_____

_____

What changes do you need to make? Course correction is easier before it gets out of control!

_____

_____

_____

_____

_____

_____

_____

_____

52

Year 3 REVIEW

In Sickness and in Health

Take a picture of yourselves as a couple. Having a yearly view will allow you to see the changes that are happening over time and make course corrections. Make note of your health success and challenges over the past year.

Today _____ is _____ years old and _____ is _____ years old

_____

_____

_____

_____

_____

_____

_____

What changes do you need to make? Course correction is easier before it gets out of control!

_____

_____

_____

_____

_____

_____

_____

_____

Date: _____

In Sickness and in Health

Take a picture of yourselves as a couple. Having a yearly view will allow you to see the changes that are happening over time and make course corrections. Make note of your health success and challenges over the past year.

Today _____ is _____ years old and _____ is _____ years old

_____

_____

_____

_____

_____

_____

_____

What changes do you need to make? Course correction is easier before it gets out of control!

_____

_____

_____

_____

_____

_____

_____

_____

Year 5 REVIEW

Date: _____

In Sickness and in Health

Take a picture of yourselves as a couple. Having a yearly view will allow you to see the changes that are happening over time and make course corrections. Make note of your health success and challenges over the past year.

Today _____ is _____ years old and _____ is _____ years old

_____

_____

_____

_____

_____

_____

What changes do you need to make? Course correction is easier before it gets out of control!

_____

_____

_____

_____

_____

_____

_____

_____

_____

Year 6 REVIEW

Date: _____

In Sickness and in Health
Take a picture of yourselves as a couple. Having a yearly view will allow you to see the changes that are happening over time and make course corrections. Make note of your health success and challenges over the past year.

Today _____ is _____ years old and _____ is _____ years old

_____

_____

_____

_____

_____

_____

_____

What changes do you need to make? Course correction is easier before it gets out of control!

_____

_____

_____

_____

_____

_____

_____

_____

56

Year 7 REVIEW

Date: _____

In Sickness and in Health

Take a picture of yourselves as a couple. Having a yearly view will allow you to see the changes that are happening over time and make course corrections. Make note of your health success and challenges over the past year.

Today _____ is _____ years old and _____ is _____ years old

_____

_____

_____

_____

_____

_____

_____

What changes do you need to make? Course correction is easier before it gets out of control!

_____

_____

_____

_____

_____

_____

_____

_____

_____

Year 8 REVIEW

Date: _____

In Sickness and in Health

Take a picture of yourselves as a couple. Having a yearly view will allow you to see the changes that are happening over time and make course corrections. Make note of your health success and challenges over the past year.

Today _____ is _____ years old and _____ is _____ years old

_____

_____

_____

_____

_____

_____

_____

What changes do you need to make? Course correction is easier before it gets out of control!

_____

_____

_____

_____

_____

_____

_____

_____

Year 9 REVIEW

Date: _____

In Sickness and in Health

Take a picture of yourselves as a couple. Having a yearly view will allow you to see the changes that are happening over time and make course corrections. Make note of your health success and challenges over the past year.

Today _____ is _____ years old and _____ is _____ years old

_____

_____

_____

_____

_____

_____

_____

What changes do you need to make? Course correction is easier before it gets out of control!

_____

_____

_____

_____

_____

_____

_____

_____

Date: _____

In Sickness and in Health

Take a picture of yourselves as a couple. Having a yearly view will allow you to see the changes that are happening over time and make course corrections. Make note of your health success and challenges over the past year.

Today _____ is _____ years old and _____ is _____ years old

_____

_____

_____

_____

_____

_____

_____

What changes do you need to make? Course correction is easier before it gets out of control!

_____

_____

_____

_____

_____

_____

_____

_____

Date: _____

In Sickness and in Health

Take a picture of yourselves as a couple. Having a yearly view will allow you to see the changes that are happening over time and make course corrections. Make note of your health success and challenges over the past year.

Today _____ is _____ years old and _____ is _____ years old

_____

_____

_____

_____

_____

_____

_____

What changes do you need to make? Course correction is easier before it gets out of control!

_____

_____

_____

_____

_____

_____

_____

_____

Date: _____

In Sickness and in Health

Take a picture of yourselves as a couple. Having a yearly view will allow you to see the changes that are happening over time and make course corrections. Make note of your health success and challenges over the past year.

Today _____ is _____ years old and _____ is _____ years old

_____

_____

_____

_____

_____

_____

_____

What changes do you need to make? Course correction is easier before it gets out of control!

_____

_____

_____

_____

_____

_____

_____

_____

_____

Year 13 REVIEW

Date: _____

In Sickness and in Health

Take a picture of yourselves as a couple. Having a yearly view will allow you to see the changes that are happening over time and make course corrections. Make note of your health success and challenges over the past year.

Today _____ is _____ years old and _____ is _____ years old

_____

_____

_____

_____

_____

_____

_____

What changes do you need to make? Course correction is easier before it gets out of control!

_____

_____

_____

_____

_____

_____

_____

_____

_____

Year 14 REVIEW

In Sickness and in Health
Take a picture of yourselves as a couple. Having a yearly view will allow you to see the changes that are happening over time and make course corrections. Make note of your health success and challenges over the past year.

Today _____ is _____ years old and _____ is _____ years old

_____

_____

_____

_____

_____

_____

_____

_____

What changes do you need to make? Course correction is easier before it gets out of control!

_____

_____

_____

_____

_____

_____

_____

_____

Year 15 REVIEW

In Sickness and in Health

Take a picture of yourselves as a couple. Having a yearly view will allow you to see the changes that are happening over time and make course corrections. Make note of your health success and challenges over the past year.

Today _____ is _____ years old and _____ is _____ years old

_____

_____

_____

_____

_____

_____

_____

_____

What changes do you need to make? Course correction is easier before it gets out of control!

_____

_____

_____

_____

_____

_____

_____

_____

_____

Year 16 REVIEW

Date: _____

In Sickness and in Health

Take a picture of yourselves as a couple. Having a yearly view will allow you to see the changes that are happening over time and make course corrections. Make note of your health success and challenges over the past year.

Today _____ is _____ years old and _____ is _____ years old

_____

_____

_____

_____

_____

_____

_____

What changes do you need to make? Course correction is easier before it gets out of control!

_____

_____

_____

_____

_____

_____

_____

_____

Year 17 REVIEW

Date: _____

Today _____ is _____ years old and _____ is _____ years old

_____

_____

_____

_____

_____

_____

_____

What changes do you need to make? Course correction is easier before it gets out of control!

_____

_____

_____

_____

_____

_____

_____

_____

Year 18 REVIEW

Date: _____

In Sickness and in Health
Take a picture of yourselves as a couple. Having a yearly view will allow you to see the changes that are happening over time and make course corrections. Make note of your health success and challenges over the past year.

Today _____ is _____ years old and _____ is _____ years old

_____

_____

_____

_____

_____

_____

_____

What changes do you need to make? Course correction is easier before it gets out of control!

_____

_____

_____

_____

_____

_____

_____

_____

Year 19 REVIEW

Date: _____

In Sickness and in Health
Take a picture of yourselves as a couple. Having a yearly view will allow you to see the changes that are happening over time and make course corrections. Make note of your health success and challenges over the past year.

Today _____ is _____ years old and _____ is _____ years old

_____

_____

_____

_____

_____

_____

_____

What changes do you need to make? Course correction is easier before it gets out of control!

_____

_____

_____

_____

_____

_____

_____

_____

Year 20 REVIEW

Date: _____

In Sickness and in Health

Take a picture of yourselves as a couple. Having a yearly view will allow you to see the changes that are happening over time and make course corrections. Make note of your health success and challenges over the past year.

Today _____ is _____ years old and _____ is _____ years old

_____

_____

_____

_____

_____

_____

What changes do you need to make? Course correction is easier before it gets out of control!

_____

_____

_____

_____

_____

_____

_____

_____

Year 21 REVIEW

Date: _____

In Sickness and in Health
Take a picture of yourselves as a couple. Having a yearly view will allow you to see the changes that are happening over time and make course corrections. Make note of your health success and challenges over the past year.

Today _____ is _____ years old and _____ is _____ years old

_____

_____

_____

_____

_____

_____

_____

What changes do you need to make? Course correction is easier before it gets out of control!

_____

_____

_____

_____

_____

_____

_____

_____

Date: _____

In Sickness and in Health
Take a picture of yourselves as a couple. Having a yearly view will allow you to see the changes that are happening over time and make course corrections. Make note of your health success and challenges over the past year.

Today _____ is _____ years old and _____ is _____ years old

_____

_____

_____

_____

_____

_____

_____

What changes do you need to make? Course correction is easier before it gets out of control!

_____

_____

_____

_____

_____

_____

_____

Date: _____

In Sickness and in Health
Take a picture of yourselves as a couple. Having a yearly view will allow you to see the changes that are happening over time and make course corrections. Make note of your health success and challenges over the past year.

Today _____ is _____ years old and _____ is _____ years old

_____

_____

_____

_____

_____

_____

_____

What changes do you need to make? Course correction is easier before it gets out of control!

_____

_____

_____

_____

_____

_____

_____

_____

Year 24 REVIEW

Date: _____

In Sickness and in Health

Take a picture of yourselves as a couple. Having a yearly view will allow you to see the changes that are happening over time and make course corrections. Make note of your health success and challenges over the past year.

Today _____ is _____ years old and _____ is _____ years old

_____

_____

_____

_____

_____

_____

_____

What changes do you need to make? Course correction is easier before it gets out of control!

_____

_____

_____

_____

_____

_____

_____

_____

_____

Year 25 REVIEW

Date: _____

In Sickness and in Health

Take a picture of yourselves as a couple. Having a yearly view will allow you to see the changes that are happening over time and make course corrections. Make note of your health success and challenges over the past year.

Today _____ is _____ years old and _____ is _____ years old

_____

_____

_____

_____

_____

_____

_____

What changes do you need to make? Course correction is easier before it gets out of control!

_____

_____

_____

_____

_____

_____

_____

_____

Money - For Richer or Poorer

How rich or how poor you are will depend on how well you work together when discussing money. How well you talk about money will determine how well you build the life of your dreams. Money is a tool that you use to make your dream life. How much do you need to create your vision? Who is going to be responsible for your money as a couple? Successful couples both have a part in keeping track of expenses.

Unfortunately, while making funeral arrangements, I've discovered too many spouses that didn't know what was going on with their money. This lack of knowledge complicates an already difficult time for them. Their spouse, who was supposed to love them, died and dumped a financial crisis on them.

I met with Patricia, who came back to me a couple of weeks after I buried her husband. She asked if I would show her how to write a check. She was too embarrassed to ask her kids because her husband took care of the finances. She never asked him what was going on, and he never told her what to do about their finances. Patricia learned she had money, but she couldn't pay the bills.

Mike came in to pay for his wife's funeral expenses, and every card he tried was declined. When he went to the bank, he learned there were only a few hundred dollars in his accounts. You see, Mike had left his wife in charge of the finances. He brought home a paycheck, gave it to her, and she paid the bills, never asking what she was doing. Mike assumed that she was saving a part of the money, but after she passed away, he realized that his wife had a shopping problem and was spending every cent and then some. How sad that he did not have the foresight to share the money responsibility.

Another customer, Susan, asked me if I knew anyone who could help her get into her computer to access her finances because she didn't know how. Her husband gave her a monthly stipend to run the household each month. He died towards the end of the month, and she didn't have enough to pay next month's bills.

She later found out they were worth millions, and while he had scrimped for years, they could have lived somewhere else besides the old run-down house they lived in. Her husband had invested his income and sacrificed until the last day; he chose to earn money instead of living life. Susan now has many regrets about not becoming more involved with their finances.

Now, this is not always the case. I have talked to just as many spouses who know where their assets are. They talked and planned and lived their lives to the fullest while having enough money to build their dreams.

I spoke to Betty, whose husband died, and I was helping her get him back to the United States. They worked and planned their finances together. He was into Formula One racing, and she always wanted to experience exotic locations. He retired from working and began helping at Formula One races all over the world. They traveled to different locations around the globe to witness live events. When he got sick with cancer, they kept to their plan and did as much as they could. He was able to go to the last race track on his bucket list, and she was excited to go on the cruise she had always wanted. He died overseas, but there were no regrets, only gratitude for all they were able to do.

One of the best things you can do is develop a habit of talking about your money. When you can communicate about money and make decisions backed by supporting choices, you will be amazed at what will happen with your finances. My wife and I found that talking about money has helped us in other areas of communication as well. The excellent benefit is having more money and using it in a way that brings our dream life into a reality.

Budgeting takes commitment, just like the day you made your vows. On your first day as a couple you committed that you would begin building your life together. Don't let money be the reason your dreams split into pieces.

If you would like more information about our personal successful budgeting process, download this free handout. Visit https://mybucketjournals.com/budget-ideas

Your Finances in 25 Years

It can be rewarding as you work towards your financial goals, as a couple. It's also less stressful when someone else shares the responsibility.

How much money do you want in savings and investments in 25 years? Do you need to hire a financial planner to help you achieve this?

_____

_____

_____

_____

_____

_____

_____

_____

What is your monthly income goal in 25 years? What do you need to do to get there?

_____

_____

_____

_____

_____

_____

_____

Your Finances in 25 Years

It can be rewarding as you work towards your financial goals, as a couple. It's also less stressful when someone else shares the responsibility.

Will this income be from one or both of you working? How will having children affect these plans?

_____

_____

_____

_____

_____

_____

_____

_____

_____

Will you have any debt? For what purpose?

_____

_____

_____

_____

_____

Your Finances in 25 Years

It can be rewarding as you work towards your financial goals, as a couple. It's also less stressful when someone else shares the responsibility.

What type of investments do you want to have? Cash, rental properties, stocks, retirement, etc.

_____

_____

_____

_____

_____

_____

_____

_____

_____

_____

_____

_____

_____

_____

_____

Your Career Path

What type of career do you want?

_____

_____

_____

_____

_____

_____

_____

Is there a limit to how far you can take this career?

_____

_____

Do you want to be a manager for a company, or are you happy with a 9 to 5 job that lets you come home without worries each night?

_____

_____

_____

_____

_____

_____

Your Career Path

Do you want to own your own business?

_____

_____

_____

_____

_____

_____

_____

_____

_____

What training do you need to accomplish this?

_____

_____

_____

_____

_____

_____

_____

Master list of career accomplishments

Year 1 REVIEW

Date: _____

Money: For Richer or Poorer
Review your career path, home, and financial situations from the past year and write down your successes. How much money did you put in savings? Did you purchase a house? Was a retirement account started? Did you pay off any debt?

_____

_____

_____

_____

_____

_____

_____

Money Matters:
Based on your initial 25 year goals, what changes do you need to make to stay on target?

_____

_____

_____

_____

_____

_____

_____

_____

Year 2 REVIEW

Date: _____

Money: For Richer or Poorer
Review your career path, home, and financial situations from the past year and write down your successes. How much money did you put in savings? Did you purchase a house? Was a retirement account started? Did you pay off any debt?

_____

_____

_____

_____

_____

_____

_____

_____

Money Matters:
Based on your initial 25 year goals, what changes do you need to make to stay on target?

_____

_____

_____

_____

_____

_____

_____

_____

_____

Year 3 REVIEW

Date: _____

Money: For Richer or Poorer

Review your career path, home, and financial situations from the past year and write down your successes. How much money did you put in savings? Did you purchase a house? Was a retirement account started? Did you pay off any debt?

_____

_____

_____

_____

_____

_____

_____

Money Matters:

Based on your initial 25 year goals, what changes do you need to make to stay on target?

_____

_____

_____

_____

_____

_____

_____

_____

Year 4 REVIEW

Date: _____

Money: For Richer or Poorer
Review your career path, home, and financial situations from the past year and write down your successes. How much money did you put in savings? Did you purchase a house? Was a retirement account started? Did you pay off any debt?

_____

_____

_____

_____

_____

_____

_____

Money Matters:
Based on your initial 25 year goals, what changes do you need to make to stay on target?

_____

_____

_____

_____

_____

_____

_____

_____

Year 5 REVIEW

Date: _____

Money: For Richer or Poorer

Review your career path, home, and financial situations from the past year and write down your successes. How much money did you put in savings? Did you purchase a house? Was a retirement account started? Did you pay off any debt?

_____

_____

_____

_____

_____

_____

_____

Money Matters:

Based on your initial 25 year goals, what changes do you need to make to stay on target?

_____

_____

_____

_____

_____

_____

_____

_____

Year 6 REVIEW

Date: _____

Money: For Richer or Poorer

Review your career path, home, and financial situations from the past year and write down your successes. How much money did you put in savings? Did you purchase a house? Was a retirement account started? Did you pay off any debt?

_____

_____

_____

_____

_____

_____

_____

Money Matters:

Based on your initial 25 year goals, what changes do you need to make to stay on target?

_____

_____

_____

_____

_____

_____

_____

_____

Year 7 REVIEW

Date: _____

Money: For Richer or Poorer

Review your career path, home, and financial situations from the past year and write down your successes. How much money did you put in savings? Did you purchase a house? Was a retirement account started? Did you pay off any debt?

_____

_____

_____

_____

_____

_____

_____

Money Matters:

Based on your initial 25 year goals, what changes do you need to make to stay on target?

_____

_____

_____

_____

_____

_____

_____

Year 8 REVIEW

Date: _____

Money: For Richer or Poorer
Review your career path, home, and financial situations from the past year and write down your successes. How much money did you put in savings? Did you purchase a house? Was a retirement account started? Did you pay off any debt?

_____

_____

_____

_____

_____

_____

_____

Money Matters:
Based on your initial 25 year goals, what changes do you need to make to stay on target?

_____

_____

_____

_____

_____

_____

_____

_____

Year 9 REVIEW

Date: _____

Money: For Richer or Poorer
Review your career path, home, and financial situations from the past year and write down your successes. How much money did you put in savings? Did you purchase a house? Was a retirement account started? Did you pay off any debt?

_____

_____

_____

_____

_____

_____

_____

_____

Money Matters:
Based on your initial 25 year goals, what changes do you need to make to stay on target?

_____

_____

_____

_____

_____

_____

_____

_____

_____

_____

Year 10 REVIEW

Date: _____

Money: For Richer or Poorer
Review your career path, home, and financial situations from the past year and write down your successes. How much money did you put in savings? Did you purchase a house? Was a retirement account started? Did you pay off any debt?

_____

_____

_____

_____

_____

_____

_____

Money Matters:
Based on your initial 25 year goals, what changes do you need to make to stay on target?

_____

_____

_____

_____

_____

_____

_____

_____

Date: _____

Money: For Richer or Poorer
Review your career path, home, and financial situations from the past year and write down your successes. How much money did you put in savings? Did you purchase a house? Was a retirement account started? Did you pay off any debt?

_____

_____

_____

_____

_____

_____

_____

Money Matters:
Based on your initial 25 year goals, what changes do you need to make to stay on target?

_____

_____

_____

_____

_____

_____

_____

_____

Year 12 REVIEW

Date: _____

Money: For Richer or Poorer
Review your career path, home, and financial situations from the past year and write down your successes. How much money did you put in savings? Did you purchase a house? Was a retirement account started? Did you pay off any debt?

_____

_____

_____

_____

_____

_____

_____

Money Matters:
Based on your initial 25 year goals, what changes do you need to make to stay on target?

_____

_____

_____

_____

_____

_____

_____

_____

Year 13 REVIEW

Date: _____

Money: For Richer or Poorer

Review your career path, home, and financial situations from the past year and write down your successes. How much money did you put in savings? Did you purchase a house? Was a retirement account started? Did you pay off any debt?

_____

_____

_____

_____

_____

_____

_____

Money Matters:

Based on your initial 25 year goals, what changes do you need to make to stay on target?

_____

_____

_____

_____

_____

_____

_____

_____

_____

Year 14 REVIEW

Date: _____

Money: For Richer or Poorer

Review your career path, home, and financial situations from the past year and write down your successes. How much money did you put in savings? Did you purchase a house? Was a retirement account started? Did you pay off any debt?

_____

_____

_____

_____

_____

_____

_____

Money Matters:

Based on your initial 25 year goals, what changes do you need to make to stay on target?

_____

_____

_____

_____

_____

_____

_____

_____

Year 15 REVIEW

Date: _____

Money: For Richer or Poorer

Review your career path, home, and financial situations from the past year and write down your successes. How much money did you put in savings? Did you purchase a house? Was a retirement account started? Did you pay off any debt?

_____

_____

_____

_____

_____

_____

_____

Money Matters:

Based on your initial 25 year goals, what changes do you need to make to stay on target?

_____

_____

_____

_____

_____

_____

_____

_____

Year 16 REVIEW

Date: _____

Money: For Richer or Poorer

Review your career path, home, and financial situations from the past year and write down your successes. How much money did you put in savings? Did you purchase a house? Was a retirement account started? Did you pay off any debt?

_____

_____

_____

_____

_____

_____

_____

Money Matters:

Based on your initial 25 year goals, what changes do you need to make to stay on target?

_____

_____

_____

_____

_____

_____

_____

_____

Year 17 REVIEW

Date: _____

Money: For Richer or Poorer
Review your career path, home, and financial situations from the past year and write down your successes. How much money did you put in savings? Did you purchase a house? Was a retirement account started? Did you pay off any debt?

_____

_____

_____

_____

_____

_____

_____

Money Matters:
Based on your initial 25 year goals, what changes do you need to make to stay on target?

_____

_____

_____

_____

_____

_____

_____

_____

Year 18 REVIEW

Date: _____

Money: For Richer or Poorer

Review your career path, home, and financial situations from the past year and write down your successes. How much money did you put in savings? Did you purchase a house? Was a retirement account started? Did you pay off any debt?

_____

_____

_____

_____

_____

_____

_____

Money Matters:

Based on your initial 25 year goals, what changes do you need to make to stay on target?

_____

_____

_____

_____

_____

_____

_____

_____

Year 19 REVIEW

Date: _____

Money: For Richer or Poorer

Review your career path, home, and financial situations from the past year and write down your successes. How much money did you put in savings? Did you purchase a house? Was a retirement account started? Did you pay off any debt?

_____

_____

_____

_____

_____

_____

_____

_____

Money Matters:

Based on your initial 25 year goals, what changes do you need to make to stay on target?

_____

_____

_____

_____

_____

_____

_____

_____

_____

Date: _____

Mon

Review ... down ... house ...

... situations from the past year and write ... u put in savings? Did you purchase a ... you pay off any debt?

Money Matters:
Based on your initial 25 year goals, what changes do you need to make to stay on target?

_____

_____

_____

_____

_____

_____

_____

_____

Year 21 REVIEW

Date: _____

Money: For Richer or Poorer

Review your career path, home, and financial situations from the past year and write down your successes. How much money did you put in savings? Did you purchase a house? Was a retirement account started? Did you pay off any debt?

_____

_____

_____

_____

_____

_____

_____

Money Matters:

Based on your initial 25 year goals, what changes do you need to make to stay on target?

_____

_____

_____

_____

_____

_____

_____

_____

Date: _____

Money: For Richer or Poorer

Review your career path, home, and financial situations from the past year and write down your successes. How much money did you put in savings? Did you purchase a house? Was a retirement account started? Did you pay off any debt?

_____

_____

_____

_____

_____

_____

_____

Money Matters:

Based on your initial 25 year goals, what changes do you need to make to stay on target?

_____

_____

_____

_____

_____

_____

_____

_____

_____

Year 23 REVIEW

Date: _____

Money: For Richer or Poorer

Review your career path, home, and financial situations from the past year and write down your successes. How much money did you put in savings? Did you purchase a house? Was a retirement account started? Did you pay off any debt?

_____

_____

_____

_____

_____

_____

_____

Money Matters:

Based on your initial 25 year goals, what changes do you need to make to stay on target?

_____

_____

_____

_____

_____

_____

_____

Year 24 REVIEW

Date: _____

Money: For Richer or Poorer
Review your career path, home, and financial situations from the past year and write down your successes. How much money did you put in savings? Did you purchase a house? Was a retirement account started? Did you pay off any debt?

_____

_____

_____

_____

_____

_____

_____

_____

Money Matters:
Based on your initial 25 year goals, what changes do you need to make to stay on target?

_____

_____

_____

_____

_____

_____

_____

_____

_____

Year 25 REVIEW

Date: _____

Money: For Richer or Poorer

Review your career path, home, and financial situations from the past year and write down your successes. How much money did you put in savings? Did you purchase a house? Was a retirement account started? Did you pay off any debt?

_____

_____

_____

_____

_____

_____

_____

Money Matters:

Based on your initial 25 year goals, what changes do you need to make to stay on target?

_____

_____

_____

_____

_____

_____

_____

_____

Thoughts and Actions
To Love and To Cherish

What did you do to catch your spouse's eye? How did it make you feel when you first kissed? How much talking about your dreams and aspirations are you doing? What are you doing to show your spouse you love and cherish them?

I can tell you this effort shouldn't stop after you get married. It may not be as frequent, but it should still occur. To love and to cherish is the lifelong pursuit of a happy couple.

I learned a great example of this one day during a funeral arrangement with Jim when we talked about his wife. During our meeting he was speaking, and then his cell phone went off for a 9 am alarm. He stopped talking and was unresponsive; then, tears ran down his cheeks. After a couple of moments, I asked him if he was okay. He said yes and slowly picked up his phone to turn off the alert.

You see, this was the first day since his retirement that he didn't get to kiss his wife at 9 am. He explained that when they first purchased cell phones, they programmed an alarm for 9 am every day. When it sounded, they would stop what they were doing, wherever they were, and give thanks for each other. They added the daily kiss after he retired. Then at 3 pm, another alarm reminded them to stop and give thanks for their life together and ask for peace in the world. They did this every day for years, as an audible reminder of how lucky they were to have each other.

What are some of the small things that you can do that will help you remember how lucky you felt when you were getting married? How can you cherish the person you have chosen to grow old with and create the way you want your life to be?

I believe that marriage is for you to help your spouse grow. I've mentioned that there will be good times and times of struggle. In your marriage, you will have times that things won't go right, and you will learn a lesson from someone who loves you. As you will continue to develop your trust, faith, and honesty with your spouse, one of the lessons will be forgiveness. At different times you might do something to hurt the other's feelings. You may be the one hurting that person's feelings or the one getting hurt. You may be the one asking for forgiveness or the one giving forgiveness. When this happens, it is a failed interaction with your spouse. Make up, learn from it and move on - together.

I learned a valuable lesson from Will Smith; he said to "fail often, fail early, and fail forward." This sentiment will help you in the growth of your relationship. Knowing that you will have failures in your marriage doesn't mean it is the end. If you need to make mistakes early in your marriage, do it often, and then take steps so they never happen again, or at least less frequently. It will strengthen your relationship and teach you what you shouldn't be doing or saying to hurt your spouse's feelings.

It takes two to bring out the best in each other. You are not perfect, and your spouse is not perfect. Everyone is a work in process, and needs to have imperfections chipped away and ground off. Working together can put on the polishing touches of how we interact. The beauty of marriage is you have someone by your side to help you. If you honor each other as equals and decide to help each other become the best person, your marriage will bring you joy, happiness, and strength that will help you during your struggles.

> "Be very careful about what you think. Your thoughts run your life." Anonymous

Our Thoughts Become Things

Be mindful of your thoughts because they will trick you. If you think about something and then add your emotions to the idea, it will become real. For example, if you believe your spouse is lazy, you get mad about it. What do you think you will see? You will only focus on the times that they are sitting around or wasting time, which often makes you blind to what they are trying to become. Your thoughts and emotions can bring joy or hardness to your heart.

Remember, are you helping each other grow into the best person you can be. Watch your thoughts and always ask yourself, is this helping us get to where we want to go? When negative thoughts and emotions are in the way, you won't want to help that person, and a distancing begins. Communication is critical here. If you can talk about money and work together, then you will be able to talk about things that bother each other. Discuss how best to resolve the situation and grow from that experience. It will prepare you for the next time it comes up. You never stop learning from each other and never stop helping each other.

A struggle in your life is the test of how strong and resilient your relationship is at that moment. The past doesn't matter, except to look back and remember what you have learned. The future is what you are becoming. The moment you are in now will pass, learn from it, enjoy it, and have peace that it will be in the past sooner than later.

I worked with Joan to help hold funeral services for her husband. I talked with her for several days and learned that a few years before their son died suddenly. Death of a child can often cause a strained marriage and, eventually, divorce. This couple went in the opposite direction. They began working more closely, and she quit her job to work more with her husband. He was a golfer, and she became a golfer. They started working and fulfilling his dream to play all over the world. It was also fulfilling her desire to see the world and to travel. When he got sick, they continued until he could no longer fly. At the funeral, I had attendees come up and tell me how great they were as a couple and how they changed after their son died. They were more in love with each other, and their relationship grew in leaps and bounds from this challenge. Their life became richer for that shared experience.

You are working together to build a life. The view you both created together is clearly in front of you. You have created the goal with your thoughts and dreams. If you don't watch your thoughts, you may quit on this journey before it ends. One of the most significant powers you have is to tell a negative thought, "NO, this is not helping me." When negativity happens, take a deep breath and ask yourself what will move your marriage forward. An answer will come, follow it. That's your intuition helping you.

You Can't Love and Cherish without Romance, Intimacy, and Sex.

Romance strengthens the bond between both of you. It doesn't stop after the honeymoon or first year of marriage but is something that has to continue to be nurtured by both of you. Intimacy isn't the responsibility of one or the other of you.

You can't ignore this component in your marriage. The closeness that you have at the beginning may change, but romance, intimacy, and sex must remain a part of it. It is the one act that is not shared with other people. Intimacy is uniquely giving of yourself and should be for this relationship only.

Continued intimacy will boost each other's self-confidence; it shows you are loved, wanted, and accepted, no matter what other faults, traits, or talents you are working to improve. Over the years, things will change as you change, and adjustments will occur in the romance, intimacy, and sex area of your life. It will be up to both of you to figure out how it will best serve to move your relationship and dreams forward.

What are your meaningful relationships?

Do you want children, how many?

_____

_____

_____

_____

_____

_____

How will you relate with your spouse, friends, children, and grandchildren? Describe the relationship you want to have with each of these people.

_____

_____

_____

_____

_____

_____

_____

Are large family gatherings important to you? What will you do for holidays?

_____

_____

_____

_____

_____

_____

_____

_____

How about living close to other family members?

_____

_____

_____

_____

_____

_____

_____

Year 1 REVIEW

Date: _____

Relationships, Rules, Giving: To Love and To Cherish
What relationship milestones did you accomplish in the past year? How are you giving of yourself to others?

_____

_____

_____

_____

_____

_____

_____

_____

Are there any new rules you need to create to help your marriage be stronger?

_____

_____

_____

_____

_____

_____

_____

_____

Year 2 REVIEW

Date: _____

Relationships, Rules, Giving: To Love and To Cherish

What relationship milestones did you accomplish in the past year? How are you giving of yourself to others?

_____

_____

_____

_____

_____

_____

_____

_____

Are there any new rules you need to create to help your marriage be stronger?

_____

_____

_____

_____

_____

_____

_____

_____

Year 3 REVIEW

Date: _____

Relationships, Rules, Giving: To Love and To Cherish
What relationship milestones did you accomplish in the past year? How are you giving of yourself to others?

_____

_____

_____

_____

_____

_____

_____

_____

Are there any new rules you need to create to help your marriage be stronger?

_____

_____

_____

_____

_____

_____

_____

_____

_____

Year 4 REVIEW

Date: _____

Relationships, Rules, Giving: To Love and To Cherish

What relationship milestones did you accomplish in the past year? How are you giving of yourself to others?

_____

_____

_____

_____

_____

_____

_____

_____

Are there any new rules you need to create to help your marriage be stronger?

_____

_____

_____

_____

_____

_____

_____

_____

_____

Year 5 REVIEW

Date: _____

Relationships, Rules, Giving: To Love and To Cherish
What relationship milestones did you accomplish in the past year? How are you giving of yourself to others?

_____

_____

_____

_____

_____

_____

_____

Are there any new rules you need to create to help your marriage be stronger?

_____

_____

_____

_____

_____

_____

_____

_____

Year 6 REVIEW

Date: _____

Relationships, Rules, Giving: To Love and To Cherish
What relationship milestones did you accomplish in the past year? How are you giving of yourself to others?

_____

_____

_____

_____

_____

_____

_____

_____

Are there any new rules you need to create to help your marriage be stronger?

_____

_____

_____

_____

_____

_____

_____

_____

_____

Year 7 REVIEW

Date: _____

Relationships, Rules, Giving: To Love and To Cherish

What relationship milestones did you accomplish in the past year? How are you giving of yourself to others?

_____

_____

_____

_____

_____

_____

_____

Are there any new rules you need to create to help your marriage be stronger?

_____

_____

_____

_____

_____

_____

_____

_____

_____

Year 8 REVIEW

Date: _____

Relationships, Rules, Giving: To Love and To Cherish
What relationship milestones did you accomplish in the past year? How are you giving of yourself to others?

_____

_____

_____

_____

_____

_____

_____

Are there any new rules you need to create to help your marriage be stronger?

_____

_____

_____

_____

_____

_____

_____

_____

Year 9 REVIEW

Date: _____

Relationships, Rules, Giving: To Love and To Cherish
What relationship milestones did you accomplish in the past year? How are you giving of yourself to others?

_____

_____

_____

_____

_____

_____

_____

_____

Are there any new rules you need to create to help your marriage be stronger?

_____

_____

_____

_____

_____

_____

_____

_____

_____

Year 10 REVIEW

Date: _____

Relationships, Rules, Giving: To Love and To Cherish
What relationship milestones did you accomplish in the past year? How are you giving of yourself to others?

_____

_____

_____

_____

_____

_____

_____

Are there any new rules you need to create to help your marriage be stronger?

_____

_____

_____

_____

_____

_____

_____

_____

_____

Year 11 REVIEW

Date: _____

Relationships, Rules, Giving: To Love and To Cherish
What relationship milestones did you accomplish in the past year? How are you giving of yourself to others?

_____

_____

_____

_____

_____

_____

_____

_____

Are there any new rules you need to create to help your marriage be stronger?

_____

_____

_____

_____

_____

_____

_____

_____

Year 12 REVIEW

Date: _____

Relationships, Rules, Giving: To Love and To Cherish
What relationship milestones did you accomplish in the past year? How are you giving of yourself to others?

_____

_____

_____

_____

_____

_____

_____

_____

Are there any new rules you need to create to help your marriage be stronger?

_____

_____

_____

_____

_____

_____

_____

_____

Year 13 REVIEW

Date: _____

Relationships, Rules, Giving: To Love and To Cherish
What relationship milestones did you accomplish in the past year? How are you giving of yourself to others?

_____

_____

_____

_____

_____

_____

_____

_____

Are there any new rules you need to create to help your marriage be stronger?

_____

_____

_____

_____

_____

_____

_____

Year 14 REVIEW

Date: _____

Relationships, Rules, Giving: To Love and To Cherish
What relationship milestones did you accomplish in the past year? How are you giving of yourself to others?

_____

_____

_____

_____

_____

_____

_____

_____

Are there any new rules you need to create to help your marriage be stronger?

_____

_____

_____

_____

_____

_____

_____

_____

_____

Relationships, Rules, Giving: To Love and To Cherish

What relationship milestones did you accomplish in the past year? How are you giving of yourself to others?

_____

_____

_____

_____

_____

_____

_____

_____

Are there any new rules you need to create to help your marriage be stronger?

_____

_____

_____

_____

_____

_____

_____

_____

Year 16 REVIEW

Date: _____

Relationships, Rules, Giving: To Love and To Cherish
What relationship milestones did you accomplish in the past year? How are you giving of yourself to others?

_____

_____

_____

_____

_____

_____

_____

Are there any new rules you need to create to help your marriage be stronger?

_____

_____

_____

_____

_____

_____

_____

Year 17 REVIEW

Date: _____

Relationships, Rules, Giving: To Love and To Cherish
What relationship milestones did you accomplish in the past year? How are you giving of yourself to others?

_____

_____

_____

_____

_____

_____

_____

Are there any new rules you need to create to help your marriage be stronger?

_____

_____

_____

_____

_____

_____

_____

_____

Year 18 REVIEW

Date: _____

Relationships, Rules, Giving: To Love and To Cherish
What relationship milestones did you accomplish in the past year? How are you giving of yourself to others?

_____

_____

_____

_____

_____

_____

_____

_____

Are there any new rules you need to create to help your marriage be stronger?

_____

_____

_____

_____

_____

_____

_____

_____

Year 19 REVIEW

Date: _____

Relationships, Rules, Giving: To Love and To Cherish
What relationship milestones did you accomplish in the past year? How are you giving of yourself to others?

_____

_____

_____

_____

_____

_____

_____

_____

_____

Are there any new rules you need to create to help your marriage be stronger?

_____

_____

_____

_____

_____

_____

_____

_____

_____

Year 20 REVIEW

Date: _____

Relationships, Rules, Giving: To Love and To Cherish
What relationship milestones did you accomplish in the past year? How are you giving of yourself to others?

_____

_____

_____

_____

_____

_____

_____

Are there any new rules you need to create to help your marriage be stronger?

_____

_____

_____

_____

_____

_____

_____

_____

Year 21 REVIEW

Date: _____

Relationships, Rules, Giving: To Love and To Cherish

What relationship milestones did you accomplish in the past year? How are you giving of yourself to others?

_____

_____

_____

_____

_____

_____

_____

_____

Are there any new rules you need to create to help your marriage be stronger?

_____

_____

_____

_____

_____

_____

_____

_____

Year 22 REVIEW

Date: _____

Relationships, Rules, Giving: To Love and To Cherish
What relationship milestones did you accomplish in the past year? How are you giving of yourself to others?

_____

_____

_____

_____

_____

_____

_____

_____

Are there any new rules you need to create to help your marriage be stronger?

_____

_____

_____

_____

_____

_____

_____

_____

Date: _____

Relationships, Rules, Giving: To Love and To Cherish
What relationship milestones did you accomplish in the past year? How are you giving of yourself to others?

_____

_____

_____

_____

_____

_____

_____

Are there any new rules you need to create to help your marriage be stronger?

_____

_____

_____

_____

_____

_____

_____

_____

Date: _____

Relationships, Rules, Giving: To Love and To Cherish
What relationship milestones did you accomplish in the past year? How are you giving of yourself to others?

_____

_____

_____

_____

_____

_____

_____

Are there any new rules you need to create to help your marriage be stronger?

_____

_____

_____

_____

_____

_____

_____

Year 25 REVIEW

Date: _____

Relationships, Rules, Giving: To Love and To Cherish
What relationship milestones did you accomplish in the past year? How are you giving of yourself to others?

_____

_____

_____

_____

_____

_____

_____

_____

Are there any new rules you need to create to help your marriage be stronger?

_____

_____

_____

_____

_____

_____

_____

_____

_____

Our Master Bucket List

List the hobbies, trips, activities and other experiences you want to do together over the next 25 years. Use this as your master "Bucket List" to see the things you've planned at a glance.

Add Date	Description	Completed

Our Master Bucket List

List the hobbies, trips, activities and other experiences you want to do together over the next 25 years. Use this as your master "Bucket List" to see the things you've planned at a glance.

Add Date	Description	Completed

Our Master Bucket List

List the hobbies, trips, activities and other experiences you want to do together over the next 25 years. Use this as your master "Bucket List" to see the things you've planned at a glance.

Add Date	Description	Completed

Our Master Bucket List

List the hobbies, trips, activities and other experiences you want to do together over the next 25 years. Use this as your master "Bucket List" to see the things you've planned at a glance.

Add Date	Description	Completed

Our Master Bucket List

List the hobbies, trips, activities and other experiences you want to do together over the next 25 years. Use this as your master "Bucket List" to see the things you've planned at a glance.

Add Date	Description	Completed

Our Master Bucket List

List the hobbies, trips, activities and other experiences you want to do together over the next 25 years. Use this as your master "Bucket List" to see the things you've planned at a glance.

Add Date	Description	Completed

Our Master Bucket List

List the hobbies, trips, activities and other experiences you want to do together over the next 25 years. Use this as your master "Bucket List" to see the things you've planned at a glance.

Add Date	Description	Completed

Our Master Bucket List

List the hobbies, trips, activities and other experiences you want to do together over the next 25 years. Use this as your master "Bucket List" to see the things you've planned at a glance.

Add Date	Description	Completed